DIFFICULT LEVEL

MATCHING CHINESE CHARACTERS AND PINYIN

把汉字和拼音连起来

MANDARIN CHINESE PINYIN TEST SERIES

测试你的拼音知识

PART 13

Simplified Mandarin Chinese Characters with Pinyin and English, Mind Games, Test Your Knowledge of Pinyin with Multiple Answer Choice Puzzle Questions, Fast Reading & Vocabulary, Answers Included, Easy Lessons for Beginners, HSK All Levels

DENG YIXIN 邓艺心

ACKNOWLEDGEMENT

I would like to thank everyone who helped me complete this book, including my teachers, family members, friends, colleagues.

谢谢

Deng Yixin

邓艺心

INTRODUCTION

Chinese language and culture are a huge concept. In order to understand and appreciate Mandarin Chinese, we need to understand the language. Learning Chinese character is a very important part of learning the language. And, yes, learning pinyin is a must!

Welcome to **Connecting Chinese Characters and Pinyin Test Series**. Now you can test the knowledge of your Chinese pinyin (测试你的拼音知识). In these books and lessons therein, you will learn recognizing pinyin of the simplified Chinese characters. The books contain hundreds of character-pinyin matching **puzzles** (questions). For each question, there are Chinese characters in the left column and pinyin in the right column. You need to guess the correct pinyin of the given characters (把汉字和拼音连起来). The **English** meanings of the Chinese characters has been included a quick reference. The answers of all the question are provided at the end of the book.

CONTENTS

CHAPTER 1: QUESTIONS (1-30)

#1.

A. 纠   1. Bó (Rich)

B. 魅   2. Jiǔ (Collective term for the tribes of northern China)

C. 失   3. Shī (Lose)

D. 旭   4. Xù (Dawn)

E. 裕   5. Yù (Abundant)

F. 博   6. Mèi (Goblin)

#2.

A. 井   1. Jǐng (Surname)

B. 韩   2. Guà (Gown)

C. 汹   3. Tóu (Dice)

D. 裳   4. Cháng (Skirt (worn in ancient China))

E. 骰   5. Hán (South Korean)

F. 褂   6. Xiōng (Turbulent)

#3.

A. 豝   1. Bā (Hope earnestly)

B. 陆   2. Wēi (Power)

C. 巴 3. Qìn (Ooze)

D. 沁 4. Xiǎn (Wild fires)

E. 背 5. Lù (Land)

F. 威 6. Bèi (Body's back)

#4.

A. 生 1. Yě (And also)

B. 纫 2. Zhān (Glue)

C. 也 3. Shēng (Give birth to)

D. 曌 4. Zhào (The name Wu Zetian)

E. 齐 5. Jì (Flavoring)

F. 粘 6. Rèn (Thread)

#5.

A. 朗 1. Huí (Eddy)

B. 畏 2. Wèi (Fear)

C. 雅 3. Tián (Dryland)

D. 和 4. Yǎ (Refined)

E. 洄 5. Lǎng (Light)

F. 畠 6. Hé (Gentle)

#6.

A. 浑 1. Lòu (Leak)

B. 意 2. Hún (Muddy)

C. 索 3. Tīng (Spit of land)

D. 汀 4. Miǎn (Overflowing)

E. 漏 5. Yì (Meaning)

F. 沔 6. Suǒ (Cable)

#7.

A. 酶 1. Tiǎo (Gentle and graceful (of a woman))

B. 硭 2. Méi (Enzyme)

C. 尿 3. Niào (Urine)

D. 窕 4. Táng (For nothing)

E. 制 5. Zhì (Make)

F. 唐 6. Máng (A crude saltpeter)

#8.

A. 盉 1. Bǐng (Report)

B. 难 2. Zhǐ (Finger)

C. 指 3. Péi (Accompany)

D. 馥 4. Nán (Difficult)

E. 禀	5. Fù (Fragrance)

F. 陪	6. Hé (Handle)

#9.

A. 飧	1. Yǎ (Refined)

B. 雅	2. Qiān (Modest)

C. 稣	3. Ér (Lukewarm water)

D. 舡	4. Sūn (Supper)

E. 洏	5. Sū (Revive)

F. 谦	6. Chuán (Boat)

#10.

A. 汊	1. Răn (Edge of tortoise-shell)

B. 鹈	2. Chà (Branch of a river or current)

C. 黦	3. Din (Indigo)

D. 冉	4. Lā (Pull)

E. 拉	5. Tí (Pelican)

F. 靛	6. Yuè (Yellowish-black)

#11.

A. 益	1. Dǎn (Calm and honest)

B. 黕　　2. Zōu (Corner)

C. 壮　　3. Niǎn (Roller)

D. 碾　　4. Sū (Crisp)

E. 酥　　5. Zhuàng (Strong)

F. 陬　　6. Yì (Benefit)

#12.

A. 汕　　1. Wū (A surname)

B. 窿　　2. Shàn (Weir)

C. 沥　　3. Lì (Drop)

D. 邬　　4. Qǐ (Begging)

E. 鲌　　5. Bà (Spanish mackerel)

F. 乞　　6. Lóng (Gallery)

#13.

A. 怖　　1. Bù (Be afraid of)

B. 耙　　2. Lēi (Tie or strap sth. tight)

C. 旁　　3. Liǎn (An ancient vessel for broomcorn millet)

D. 泽　　4. Pá (Rake)

E. 勒　　5. Zé (Pool)

F. 琏　　6. Páng (Other)

#14.

A. 桂　　1. Táo (Pottery)

B. 辉　　2. Guì (Cassia)

C. 烈　　3. Táng (Purple)

D. 耏　　4. Huī (Brightness)

E. 匋　　5. Ér (Beard)

F. 赯　　6. Liè (Strong)

#15.

A. 富　　1. Jī (Clogs)

B. 屐　　2. Mā (Mom)

C. 板　　3. Kūn (Quinone)

D. 妈　　4. Fù (Wealth)

E. 醌　　5. Bǎn (Board)

F. 怕　　6. Pà (Fear)

#16.

A. 欸　　1. Chí (Spoon)

B. 忽　　2. Āi (Sigh)

C. 童　　3. Qì (Almost)

D. 汔 4. Tóng (Child)

E. 匙 5. Hū (Neglect)

F. 郜 6. Gào (A surname)

#17.

A. 头 1. Lěi (Build by piling up bricks, stones, earth, etc.)

B. 犄 2. Yàn (Be satisfied)

C. 厌 3. Jī (Pin down)

D. 耶 4. Piān (A piece of writing)

E. 篇 5. Tóu (Top)

F. 垒 6. Yé (At the end of a sentence (like 啊))

#18.

A. 临 1. Hén (Mark)

B. 痕 2. Xiáng (Circle in the air)

C. 脏 3. Lín (Be close to)

D. 翔 4. Mí (Waste)

E. 瘟 5. Zàng (Internal organs)

F. 靡 6. Wēn (Acute communicable diseases)

#19.

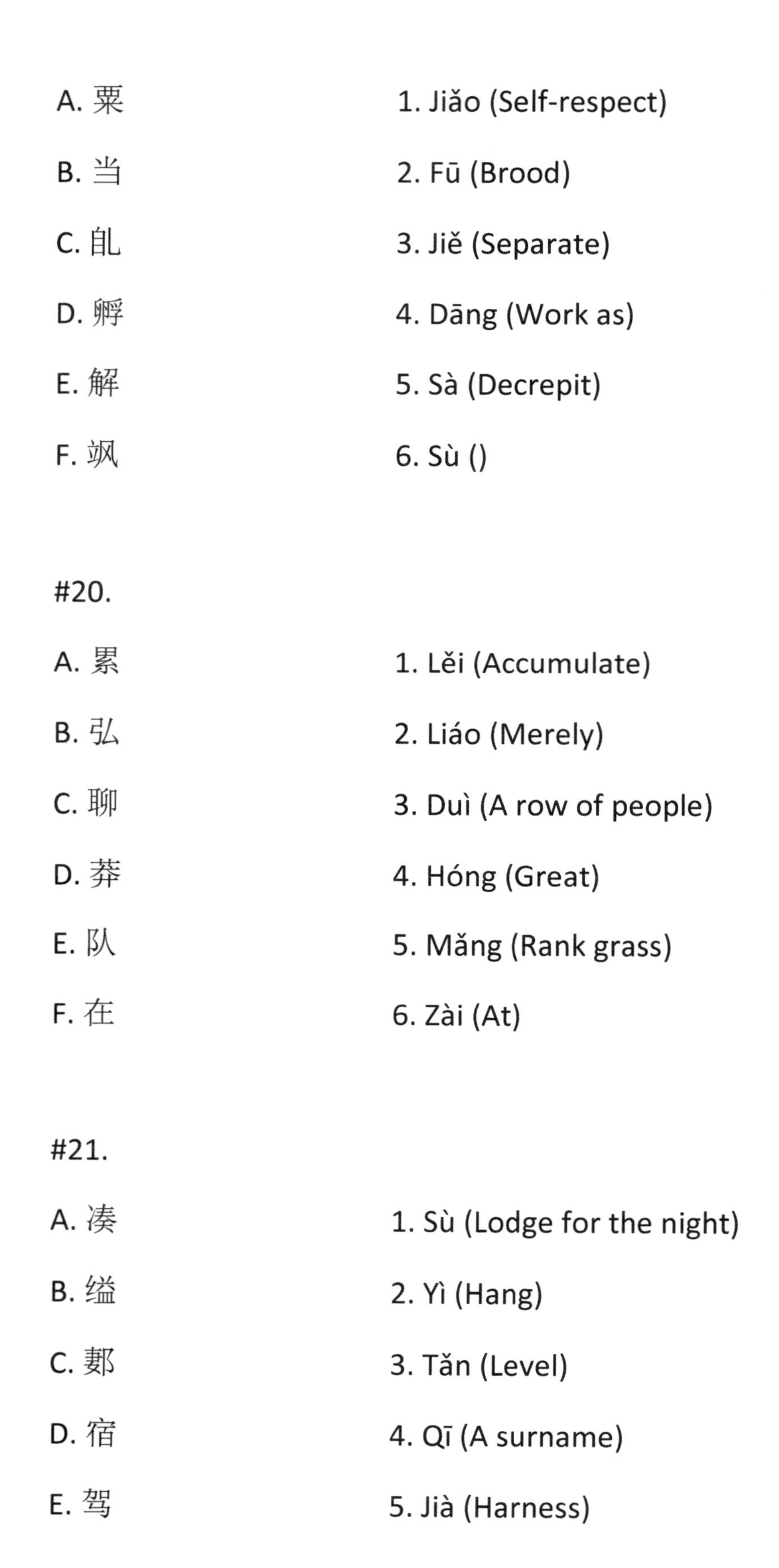

A. 粟

B. 当

C. 乩

D. 孵

E. 解

F. 飒

1. Jiǎo (Self-respect)

2. Fū (Brood)

3. Jiě (Separate)

4. Dāng (Work as)

5. Sà (Decrepit)

6. Sù ()

#20.

A. 累

B. 弘

C. 聊

D. 莽

E. 队

F. 在

1. Lěi (Accumulate)

2. Liáo (Merely)

3. Duì (A row of people)

4. Hóng (Great)

5. Mǎng (Rank grass)

6. Zài (At)

#21.

A. 凑

B. 缢

C. 郪

D. 宿

E. 驾

1. Sù (Lodge for the night)

2. Yì (Hang)

3. Tǎn (Level)

4. Qī (A surname)

5. Jià (Harness)

F. 坦　　6. Còu (Happen by chance)

#22.

A. 紊　　1. Yǐn (Hide)

B. 骭　　2. Gàn (Shank)

C. 郸　　3. Pù (Expose)

D. 隐　　4. Tǔn (Float)

E. 氽　　5. Dān (A surname)

F. 曝　　6. Wěn (Disorderly)

#23.

A. 蛛　　1. Guī (Rule)

B. 辉　　2. Jùn (Complete)

C. 竣　　3. Huī (Brightness)

D. 规　　4. Yì (Different)

E. 觊　　5. Jì (Attempt)

F. 异　　6. Zhū (Spider)

#24.

A. 污　　1. Shú (What)

B. 壳　　2. Wū (Sewage)

C. 孰 3. Biàn (Bright)

D. 支 4. Piān (A piece of writing)

E. 篇 5. Zhī (Support)

F. 昪 6. Ké (Shell)

#25.

A. 耿 1. Ěr (Er He River (in Henan Province))

B. 洱 2. Guǎn (Accommodation for guests)

C. 沬 3. Wèi (Fear)

D. 济 4. Jǐ (The Ji River)

E. 馆 5. Mèi (Capital city of the Shang Dynasty, in the present-day south Tangyin (汤阴), Henan Province)

F. 畏 6. Gěng (Shining)

#26.

A. 酌 1. Lì (A surname)

B. 留 2. Dàn (Dawn)

C. 旦 3. Zhuó (Drink)

D. 郦 4. Liú (Remain)

E. 彦 5. Huàn (Melt)

F. 涣 6. Yàn (A man of virtue and ability)

#27.

A. 赏 1. Făng (Imitate)

B. 犇 2. Gòng (Tribute)

C. 县 3. Xiàn (County)

D. 仿 4. Shăng (Grant a reward)

E. 累 5. Jǔ (Collect)

F. 贡 6. Léi (Tie)

#28.

A. 属 1. Lǐ (Sweet wine)

B. 吆 2. Yāo (Cry out)

C. 醴 3. Bèi (A word used in a place name)

D. 碚 4. Shǔ (Category)

E. 粘 5. Nián (Sticky)

F. 霜 6. Shuāng (Frost)

#29.

A. 貘 1. Mò (Tapir)

B. 弈 2. Sà (Bodhisattva)

C. 觟 3. Xiè (The legendary god sheep)

D. 窨 4. Xūn (Basement)

E. 耧 5. Yì (Play chess)

F. 萨 6. Lóu (An animal-drawn seed plough)

#30.

A. 弭 1. Zhài (Stockade)

B. 除 2. Zǐ (To cultivate the soil (on plant roots))

C. 启 3. Qǐ (Open)

D. 辽 4. Liáo (Distant)

E. 寨 5. Chú (Get rid of)

F. 耔 6. Mǐ (Quell)

CHAPTER 2: QUESTIONS (31-60)

#31.

A. 剥 1. Kū (Cry)

B. 齑 2. Jī (Fine)

C. 胃 3. Wèi (Stomach)

D. 迅 4. Xùn (Fast)

E. 哭 5. Jiē (Bear fruit)

F. 结 6. Bāo (Skin)

#32.

A. 泻 1. Yù (Myna)

B. 纂 2. Xiè (Flow swiftly)

C. 鹆 3. Téng (Bind)

D. 胳 4. Zuǎn (Compile)

E. 郦 5. Lì (A surname)

F. 縢 6. Gē (Armpit)

#33.

A. 鞘 1. Lù (Used in place names)

B. 汝 2. Yì (Easy)

C. 易 3. Zhà (For the first time)

D. 癿 | 4. Qié (A surname)

E. 乍 | 5. Rǔ (You people)

F. 六 | 6. Qiào (Sheath)

#34.

A. 戴 | 1. Yì (Assist)

B. 指 | 2. Zhǐ (Finger)

C. 曝 | 3. Liǎo (Finish)

D. 翊 | 4. Pù (Expose)

E. 晷 | 5. Guǐ (Sundial)

F. 了 | 6. Dài (Put on)

#35.

A. 脏 | 1. Xiān (Fresh)

B. 乃 | 2. Fú (Cloth scarf used as a wrap)

C. 泂 | 3. Nǎi (Be)

D. 鲜 | 4. Jiǒng (Far)

E. 魑 | 5. Chī (Man-eating mountain spirits)

F. 袱 | 6. Zàng (Internal organs)

#36.

A. 解 1. Zhì (Wisdom)

B. 憬 2. Hōng (Sound of a crash)

C. 訇 3. Chǐ (Shame)

D. 耻 4. Cì (Order)

E. 智 5. Jiě (Separate)

F. 次 6. Jǐng (Awaken)

#37.

A. 衰 1. Gāng (A surname)

B. 江 2. Yáng ()

C. 沓 3. Zú (Race)

D. 的 4. Dá (Pile)

E. 飏 5. Dì (Target)

F. 族 6. Cuī (Decrease)

#38.

A. 协 1. Jiān (Pointed)

B. 矿 2. Xié (Association)

C. 占 3. Kuàng (Ore deposit)

D. 垂 4. Chuí (Hang down)

E. 畃 5. Zhān (Practice divination)

F. 尖 6. Yún (Tidily tilled)

#39.

A. 郄 1. Xìng (Mood or desire to do sth)

B. 殊 2. Shū (Different)

C. 兴 3. Qiè (A surname)

D. 怀 4. Má (Hemp)

E. 紧 5. Jǐn (Taut)

F. 麻 6. Huái (Bosom)

#40.

A. 霄 1. Xiāo (Clouds)

B. 卸 2. Xiè (Unlade)

C. 邰 3. Jiǔ (Cauterize)

D. 挑 4. Tiǎo (Stir up)

E. 弄 5. Nòng (Do)

F. 灸 6. Tái (A surname)

#41.

A. 荥 1. Yíng (In place names)

B. 斑 2. Gè (Each)

C. 允

D. 笔

E. 各

F. 他

3. Tǐng (Scepter)

4. Tā (He)

5. Bǐ (Pen)

6. Yǔn (Allow)

#42.

A. 累

B. 捡

C. 煞

D. 蛾

E. 洑

F. 隼

1. É (Moth)

2. Fú (Undercurrent)

3. Lěi (Accumulate)

4. Capture (Catch)

5. Shā (Stop)

6. Sǔn (Falcon)

#43.

A. 难

B. 凶

C. 邢

D. 套

E. 卧

F. 解

1. Nàn (Catastrophe)

2. Wò (Lie)

3. Tào (Overlap)

4. Xiè (Understand)

5. Xiōng (Inauspicious)

6. Píng (A surname)

#44.

A. 邯 1. Xuán (Mysterious)

B. 舣 2. Lòu (Leak)

C. 漏 3. Yǐ (Ochre)

D. 泽 4. Zé (Pool)

E. 玄 5. Hán (A surname)

F. 兹 6. Zī (This)

#45.

A. 屉 1. Yā (Ah)

B. 盒 2. Biǎo (Mounting)

C. 鹫 3. Jī (Chicken)

D. 鸡 4. Tì (A food steamer with several trays)

E. 裱 5. Hé (Box)

F. 丫 6. Jiù (Vulture)

#46.

A. 沙 1. Hái (Child)

B. 猹 2. Hào (Name)

C. 孩 3. Yìn (Offspring)

D. 号 4. Shā (Sand)

E. 胤

5. Jiē (All)

F. 皆

6. Chá (A badger-like wild animal)

#47.

A. 骱

1. Tí (Raise)

B. 棕

2. Cháng (Ordinary)

C. 擘

3. Mí (Overflow)

D. 提

4. Bò (Thumb)

E. 常

5. Zōng (Brown)

F. 弥

6. Jiè (Joint of bones)

#48.

A. 悄

1. Xìng (Nature)

B. 砰

2. Pēng (Bang)

C. 欸

3. Qiāo (Quiet)

D. 瘸

4. Xiàn (Constitution)

E. 性

5. Qué (Be lame)

F. 宪

6. Ēi (Hey)

#49.

A. 摹

1. Zhì (Sincere)

B. 允 2. Mó (Trace)

C. 殃 3. Yāng (Calamity)

D. 趟 4. Tàng (Time)

E. 乢 5. Yǔn (Allow)

F. 挲 6. Gài (Beggar)

#50.

A. 配 1. Rǔ (You people)

B. 蹚 2. Shà (A tall building)

C. 厦 3. Zhà (Fraud)

D. 诈 4. Táo (Pottery)

E. 陶 5. Tàng (Ford)

F. 汝 6. Pèi (Spouse)

#51.

A. 在 1. Kāi (Open)

B. 开 2. Zài (Exist)

C. 沅 3. Běn (A bamboo or wicker scoop)

D. 畚 4. Fǎng (Visit)

E. 舢 5. Yuán (A surname)

F. 访 6. Shān (Small boat)

#52.

A. 揪 1. Yáng ()

B. 飏 2. Suǒ (Place)

C. 鸢 3. Wū (A surname)

D. 疟 4. Yuān (Kite)

E. 邬 5. Nüè (Malaria)

F. 所 6. Jiū (Pull)

#53.

A. 陈 1. Yì (后羿, hòu yì, Hou Yi)

B. 狈 2. Běn (A bamboo or wicker scoop)

C. 羿 3. Chén (Lay out)

D. 产 4. Zhǒng (Species)

E. 种 5. Chǎn (Give birth to)

F. 畚 6. Bèi (A wolf-like animal with short forelegs)

#54.

A. 涨 1. Méi (A kind of beautiful jade)

B. 沦 2. Lún (Sink)

C. 玫 3. Jú (Chessboard)

D. 刚 4. Gāng (Hard)

E. 设 5. Zhǎng (Rise)

F. 局 6. Shè (Set up)

#55.

A. 斛 1. Dá (Answer)

B. 军 2. Shuāng (Frost)

C. 鸶 3. Hú (A dry measure used in former times, originally equal to 10 dou, later 5 dou)

D. 霜 4. Jūn (Armed forces)

E. 答 5. Jù (Poor)

F. 窭 6. Sī (Egret)

#56.

A. 陴 1. Bèi (Comet)

B. 樊 2. Bèi (A word used in a place name)

C. 孛 3. Pí (Parapet)

D. 古 4. Chāo (To plagiarize)

E. 剿 5. Fán (Surname)

F. 碚 6. Gǔ (Ancient)

#57.

A. 程　　1. Yīng (Eagle)

B. 犄　　2. Zuò (Certain)

C. 皇　　3. Chéng (Rule)

D. 念　　4. Jī (Pin down)

E. 凿　　5. Niàn (Read aloud)

F. 鹰　　6. Huáng (Grand)

#58.

A. 姬　　1. Jiāng (Thick liquid)

B. 浆　　2. Píng (A surname)

C. 粪　　3. Jī (A complimentary term for women used in ancient China)

D. 扎　　4. Zhā (Prick)

E. 耋　　5. Fèn (Droppings)

F. 郱　　6. Dié (Septuagenarian)

#59.

A. 郛　　1. Jiāo (Burnt)

B. 焦　　2. Liáo (Distant)

C. 寖　　3. Bì (The flight of steps leading to the throne hall)

D. 缜 — 4. Zhěn (Careful)

E. 陛 — 5. Tiǎo (Gentle and graceful (of a woman))

F. 辽 — 6. Fú (Outer wall of a city)

#60.

A. 旬 — 1. Zhuàn (Revolve)

B. 泾 — 2. Kàng (High)

C. 粑 — 3. Xún (A period of ten days)

D. 婶 — 4. Bā (Cake)

E. 转 — 5. Jīng (Short for the Jinghe River)

F. 亢 — 6. Shěn (Aunt)

CHAPTER 3: QUESTIONS (61-90)

#61.

A. 帛	1. Bó (Silks)
B. 京	2. Jīng (The capital of a country)
C. 烊	3. Fù (Abalone)
D. 醴	4. Lǐ (Sweet wine)
E. 鳆	5. Yáng (Melt)
F. 包	6. Bāo (Wrap)

#62.

A. 笼	1. Chuǎi (Surmise)
B. 酋	2. Qiú (Chief of a tribe)
C. 揣	3. Gǎn (Catch up with)
D. 缤	4. Bīn (Abundant)
E. 赶	5. Lóng (Cage)
F. 脚	6. Jiǎo (Foot)

#63.

A. 紫	1. Méi (Matchmake)
B. 媒	2. Zǐ (Purple)

C. 罛 3. Mǎi (Buy)

D. 买 4. Gū (Large fishing nets)

E. 泌 5. Què (Crack)

F. 郤 6. Bì (Gushed spring water)

#64.

A. 扇 1. Shān (Fan)

B. 凑 2. Còu (Happen by chance)

C. 敏 3. Zào (Chirp)

D. 渤 4. Bó (Bohai Sea)

E. 嚭 5. Pǐ (Mound)

F. 噪 6. Mǐn (Quick)

#65.

A. 滋 1. Biǎo (Mounting)

B. 奔 2. Bèn (Go straight towards)

C. 裱 3. Huī (Brightness)

D. 职 4. Wō (Nest)

E. 窝 5. Zī (Taste)

F. 辉 6. Zhí (Duty)

#66.

A. 旺 1. Qiǎng (Make an effort)

B. 泥 2. Biào (Swim bladder of fish)

C. 鳔 3. Nì (Cover or daub with plaster, putty, etc.)

D. 的 4. Wàng (Prosperous)

E. 轵 5. Zhǐ (Axletree terminal)

F. 强 6. De (And so on)

#67.

A. 奇 1. Yān (A surname)

B. 觟 2. Jī (Odd)

C. 燕 3. Shǐ (History)

D. 卓 4. Xiè (The legendary god sheep)

E. 史 5. Zhuō (Table)

F. 座 6. Zuò (Seat)

#68.

A. 畈 1. Yù (A surname)

B. 攻 2. Guà (Hang)

C. 坊 3. Wù (Dislike)

D. 恶 4. Fàn (Farmland, often used in place names)

E. 尉 5. Fāng (Lane)

F. 挂 6. Gōng (Attack)

#69.

A. 欹 1. Shùn (Shun, the name of a legendary monarch in ancient China)

B. 域 2. Éi (Sigh)

C. 磨 3. Dǎo (Lead)

D. 琏 4. Liǎn (An ancient vessel for broomcorn millet)

E. 舜 5. Mò (Mill)

F. 导 6. Yù (Land within certain boundaries)

#70.

A. 麻 1. Wò (Lie)

B. 卧 2. Xī (A surname)

C. 霡 3. Má (Hemp)

D. 辈 4. Bèi (Generation in family)

E. 晕 5. Mài (A light rain)

F. 郗 6. Yùn (Halo)

#71.

A. 坐 1. Zuò (Sit)

B. 猷 | 2. Shàn (Weir)

C. 沥 | 3. Jiào (Religion)

D. 汕 | 4. Yóu (Plan)

E. 凿 | 5. Zuò (Certain)

F. 教 | 6. Lì (Drop)

#72.

A. 郛 | 1. Kè (Female (animal))

B. 歙 | 2. Fú (Outer wall of a city)

C. 饮 | 3. Shè (Inhale)

D. 掴 | 4. Guāi (Slap)

E. 骒 | 5. Yǐn (Drink)

F. 耕 | 6. Gēng (Plough)

#73.

A. 玉 | 1. Yìn (Seal)

B. 驷 | 2. Yù (Jade)

C. 印 | 3. Sì (A team of four horses)

D. 猪 | 4. Shān (Cedar)

E. 器 | 5. Zhū (Hog)

F. 杉 | 6. Qì (Implement)

#74.

A. 藻 — 1. Hún (Soul)

B. 炫 — 2. Cōng (Faculty of hearing)

C. 魂 — 3. Xuàn (Dazzle)

D. 碎 — 4. Suì (Break to pieces)

E. 聪 — 5. Zǎo (Algae)

F. 恶 — 6. Wù (Dislike)

#75.

A. 盍 — 1. Zǎo (Flea)

B. 蚤 — 2. Lì (Lynx)

C. 划 — 3. Hé (Why not)

D. 崇 — 4. Huà (Delimit)

E. 猁 — 5. Zhòng (Grow)

F. 种 — 6. Chóng (High)

#76.

A. 忆 — 1. Bǎng (Arm)

B. 删 — 2. Dí (Taxi)

C. 覃 — 3. Bò (Thumb)

D. 擘 4. Shān (Delete)

E. 膀 5. Yì (Recall)

F. 的 6. Tán (Deep)

#77.

A. 耔 1. Zǐ (To cultivate the soil (on plant roots))

B. 泷 2. Ǎo (A short Chinese-style coat or jacket)

C. 縠 3. Hú (Crepe)

D. 袄 4. Lóng (Rapids)

E. 覷 5. Qū (Narrow)

F. 驶 6. Shǐ (Drive)

#78.

A. 昔 1. Pǐ (Addiction)

B. 龁 2. Xī (Former times)

C. 冈 3. Hé (To bite)

D. 爽 4. Jì (Meter)

E. 癖 5. Gāng (Ridge (of a hill))

F. 计 6. Shuǎng (Bright)

#79.

A. 泼　　1. Lì (Crime)

B. 泡　　2. Lú (Lushui River (part of the Jinsha Jiang River (金沙江) between Sichuan and Yunnan provinces))

C. 戾　　3. Diǎn (Stand on tiptoe)

D. 娘　　4. Pō (Sprinkle)

E. 泸　　5. Pào (Bubble)

F. 踮　　6. Niáng (Ma)

#80.

A. 烹　　1. Miè (Go out)

B. 更　　2. Gēng (Change)

C. 辜　　3. Gū (Crime)

D. 田　　4. Pēng (Boil)

E. 身　　5. Tián (Field)

F. 灭　　6. Shēn (Body)

#81.

A. 絷　　1. Zhí (Tie)

B. 救　　2. Jiù (Rescue)

C. 那　　3. Dú (Blacken)

D. 黩　　4. Gū (Buy)

E. 沽 5. Jīn (Jin, a unit of weight (0.5Kg))

F. 斤 6. Nuó (A surname)

#82.

A. 沧 1. Cāng ((Of the sea) dark blue)

B. 靠 2. Kào (Lean against)

C. 阮 3. Qù (Interest)

D. 夛 4. Ruǎn (Nephew)

E. 趣 5. Qīn (Parent)

F. 亲 6. Xī (Night)

#83.

A. 昌 1. Xì (System)

B. 莽 2. Zhuàng (Form)

C. 系 3. Chāng (Prosperous)

D. 邝 4. Kuàng (A surname)

E. 状 5. Mǎng (Rank grass)

F. 诚 6. Chéng (Sincere)

#84.

A. 舁 1. Fén (Male livestock)

B. 猰 2. Yú (Carry)

C. 渗 3. Yì (Friendship)

D. 惯 4. Guàn (Be used to)

E. 谊 5. Shèn (Infiltrate)

F. 髆 6. Bó (Shoulder blade)

#85.

A. 胳 1. Tán (Shoot)

B. 蚀 2. Tuǐ (Leg)

C. 笨 3. Shū (Different)

D. 腿 4. Gē (Armpit)

E. 殊 5. Shí (Lose)

F. 弹 6. Bèn (Stupid)

#86.

A. 觍 1. Fěi (Rich with literary grace)

B. 郅 2. Tiǎn (Ashamed)

C. 斐 3. Huàn (Official)

D. 宦 4. Mò (Affectionately)

E. 脉 5. Bāo (Wrap)

F. 包 6. Zhì (A surname)

#87.

A. 煞 1. Biàn (Bright)

B. 昪 2. Shā (Stop)

C. 阵 3. Zhèn (Battle array)

D. 陉 4. Fǎ (Balance weights)

E. 砝 5. Xíng (Break in a mountain ridge)

F. 耖 6. Chào (A harrow-like implement for pulverizing soil)

#88.

A. 泵 1. Nǎi (Be)

B. 司 2. Sī (Take charge of)

C. 柜 3. Huàn (Feed)

D. 览 4. Guì (Cupboard)

E. 豢 5. Bèng (Pump (e.g. air pump, water pump))

F. 乃 6. Lǎn (Take a look at)

#89.

A. 貉 1. Zuò (Seat)

B. 座 2. Bà (Spanish mackerel)

C. 轱 3. Xún (Ten days)

D. 孟　　4. Gū (Vehicle)

E. 鲌　　5. Mèng (The first month)

F. 旬　　6. Háo (Raccoon dog)

#90.

A. 洱　　1. Zàng (Bury)

B. 邰　　2. Láng (Porch)

C. 廊　　3. Tái (A surname)

D. 葬　　4. Ěr (Er He River (in Henan Province))

E. 天　　5. Tiān (Day)

F. 霰　　6. Xiàn (Graupel)

CHAPTER 4: QUESTIONS (91-120)

#91.

A. 胜 — 1. Xiǎn (A place difficult of access)

B. 孱 — 2. Chuō (Jump)

C. 险 — 3. Shèng (Win)

D. 罗 — 4. Càn (Frail)

E. 县 — 5. Luō (A net for catching birds)

F. 踔 — 6. Xiàn (County)

#92.

A. 茶 — 1. Yǐng (Trace)

B. 却 — 2. Xù (Adding)

C. 影 — 3. Chá (Tea plant)

D. 另 — 4. Pào (Big gun)

E. 炮 — 5. Què (Step back)

F. 絮 — 6. Lìng (Another)

#93.

A. 羲 — 1. Nài (A kind of apple)

B. 柰 — 2. Lóng (Grand)

C. 隆 3. Xī (A surname)

D. 惫 4. Bèi (Exhausted)

E. 审 5. Wèi (Officer)

F. 尉 6. Shěn (Careful)

#94.

A. 怠 1. Wài (Outside)

B. 猷 2. Yóu (Plan)

C. 脏 3. Qū (Hasten)

D. 趋 4. Zāng (Dirty)

E. 豗 5. Dài (Idle)

F. 外 6. Huī (Clamor)

#95.

A. 屄 1. Líng (Hear)

B. 任 2. Bī (Vaginal orifice)

C. 钱 3. Yuán (A surname)

D. 沅 4. Rén (A surname)

E. 聆 5. Bǎ (Target)

F. 靶 6. Qián (Copper coin)

#96.

A. 硕	1. Kěn (Agree)
B. 欲	2. Wǎn (Bowl)
C. 攸	3. Shuò (Large)
D. 寂	4. Yù (Desire)
E. 碗	5. Yōu (Flowing)
F. 肯	6. Jì (Lonely)

#97.

A. 试	1. Shì (Test)
B. 骼	2. Èi (Sigh)
C. 欸	3. Jiè (Be situated between)
D. 耶	4. Táng (A surname)
E. 棠	5. Gé (Skeletons)
F. 介	6. Yē (Jesus)

#98.

A. 腼	1. Huó (Mix with water, etc.)
B. 和	2. Miǎn (Face)
C. 旒	3. Liú (Tassel)
D. 磨	4. Mò (Mill)

E. 趾 | 5. Liǎo (Finish)

F. 了 | 6. Zhǐ (Toe)

#99.

A. 习 | 1. Bǎi (Surname)

B. 散 | 2. Xí (Practice)

C. 尤 | 3. Xíng (The rising and dashing waves)

D. 百 | 4. Sàn (Break up)

E. 稽 | 5. Jī (A surname)

F. 荥 | 6. Yóu (Outstanding)

#100.

A. 每 | 1. Yāo (Demand)

B. 瓴 | 2. Líng (Water jar)

C. 搂 | 3. Yáo (Precious jade)

D. 瑶 | 4. Měi (Each)

E. 累 | 5. Lèi (Tired)

F. 要 | 6. Lǒu (Hug)

#101.

A. 含　　1. Guó (Dukedom of Guo (a vassal state of the Zhou Dynasty))

B. 虢　　2. Jī (Machine)

C. 萌　　3. Méng (Sprout)

D. 聿　　4. Yù (Then)

E. 朵　　5. Hán (Keep in the mouth)

F. 机　　6. Duǒ (Flower)

#102.

A. 豭　　1. Jí (Lean)

B. 瘠　　2. Jiā (Boar)

C. 济　　3. Jì (Cross a river)

D. 蜘　　4. Rǔ (You people)

E. 汝　　5. Dù (Degree (temperature))

F. 度　　6. Zhī (Spider)

#103.

A. 开　　1. Jiù (Rescue)

B. 勼　　2. Xī (Pig)

C. 监　　3. Jiàn (An imperial office)

D. 未　　4. Jiū (Gather)

E. 豨 5. Kāi (Open)

F. 救 6. Wèi (Not)

#104.

A. 媒 1. Shòu (Receive)

B. 怠 2. Zhǎng (Palm)

C. 硌 3. gé (Clams)

D. 掌 4. Luò (Large stone)

E. 受 5. Dài (Idle)

F. 蛤 6. Méi (Matchmake)

#105.

A. 驴 1. Shì (A horizontal bar in front of a carriage for armrest)

B. 霈 2. Nàn (Catastrophe)

C. 轼 3. Pèi (Heavy rain)

D. 燕 4. Qiě (And)

E. 且 5. Yān (A surname)

F. 难 6. Lǘ (Donkey)

#106.

A. 寞 1. Mò (Lonely)

B. 重 2. Nìng (Rather)

C. 函 3. Yōu (Deep and remote)

D. 尽 4. Hán (Case)

E. 宁 5. Zhòng (Weight)

F. 幽 6. Jìn (Exhaust)

#107.

A. 坝 1. Jiǎo (Clear and bright)

B. 皎 2. Yán (Grind)

C. 风 3. Bà (Dam)

D. 罦 4. Fú (Bird-net)

E. 厘 5. Lí (Li, a unit of length)

F. 研 6. Fēng (Wind)

#108.

A. 雰 1. gé (Clams)

B. 糊 2. Hú (Stick with paste)

C. 亩 3. Què (Step back)

D. 却 4. Ruǎn (Soft)

E. 蛤 5. Mǔ (Mu, a unit of area)

F. 软 6. Fēn (Mist)

#109.

A. 虾 1. Jì (Hope)

B. 甃 2. Zhòu (Wall of a well)

C. 冀 3. Sù (Respectful)

D. 汪 4. Xiā (Shrimp)

E. 考 5. Wāng (A surname)

F. 肃 6. Kǎo (Examine)

#110.

A. 坊 1. Fáng (Workshop)

B. 北 2. Shāo (Burn)

C. 烧 3. Tuǒ (Oval)

D. 冀 4. Jì (Hope)

E. 缳 5. Huán (Tie around with ropes)

F. 椭 6. Běi (North)

#111.

A. 赩 1. Hù (A kind of edible gourd)

B. 壓 2. Yā (Pressure)

C. 瓠 3. Xì (Red)

D. 压 4. Tì (Shave)

E. 绳 5. Mò (China ink)

F. 剃 6. Shéng (Rope)

#112.

A. 豕 1. Wài (Outside)

B. 外 2. Gān (Pleasant)

C. 裳 3. Cháng (Skirt (worn in ancient China))

D. 倚 4. Guǎn (Pipe)

E. 甘 5. Yǐ (Lean on or against)

F. 管 6. Shǐ (Pig)

#113.

A. 鄴 1. Yìn (Give water to drink)

B. 价 2. Liù (Six)

C. 陆 3. Dié (Small melon)

D. 瓞 4. Yè (An ancient place name)

E. 饮 5. Chéng (Accomplish)

F. 成 6. Jià (Price)

#114.

A. 末 1. Gài (Cover)

B. 差 2. Fèi (Baboon)

C. 狒 3. Chà (Differ from)

D. 厄 4. Wū (Lake)

E. 盖 5. Mò (Tip)

F. 隖 6. È (Strategic point)

#115.

A. 吉 1. Fěi (Slander)

B. 为 2. Wéi (Do)

C. 赦 3. Jí (Lucky)

D. 诽 4. Xiàng (Nape)

E. 项 5. Yǎn (A surname)

F. 弇 6. Shè (Remit)

#116.

A. 乖 1. Sù (Early in the morning)

B. 襁 2. Nài (But)

C. 体 3. Qiǎng (Swaddling clothes)

D. 夙 4. Guāi (Obedient)

E. 奈 5. Tǐ (Body)

F. 靖 6. Jìng (Peaceful)

#117.

A. 卓 1. Huī (Brightness)

B. 耋 2. Zhuō (Tall and erect)

C. 并 3. Jì (Hold a memorial ceremony for)

D. 祭 4. Bìng (And)

E. 隗 5. Kuí (A surname)

F. 辉 6. Dié (Septuagenarian)

#118.

A. 奈 1. Gǔ (Ancient)

B. 猩 2. Jiǔ (Collective term for the tribes of northern China during the Liao, Jin, and Yuan periods)

C. 那 3. Máng (Chinese silver grass)

D. 乣 4. Xīng (Orangutan)

E. 芒 5. Nài (But)

F. 古 6. Nā (A surname)

#119.

A. 够 1. Èi (Sigh)

B. 妹 2. Yǐn (Drink)

C. 欸 3. Gòu (Enough)

D. 叩 4. Kòu (Knock)

E. 耵 5. Dīng (Earwax)

F. 饮 6. Mèi (Sister)

CHAPTER 5: QUESTIONS (121-150)

#120.

A. 奢 1. Zài (At)

B. 毕 2. Sì (A team of four horses)

C. 在 3. Dǎo (Fall)

D. 倒 4. Bì (Complete)

E. 驷 5. Shē (Extravagant)

F. 离 6. Lí (Leave)

#121.

A. 耐 1. Xiàn (County)

B. 鳗 2. Tí (Raise)

C. 反 3. Fǎn (Reverse side)

D. 呼 4. Nài (Be able to bear or endure)

E. 提 5. Hū (Breathe out)

F. 县 6. Mán (Eel)

#122.

A. 饥 1. Jiù (Past)

B. 旧 2. Qín (The Qin Dynasty)

C. 利 3. Rǔ (Disgrace)

D. 外 4. Wài (Outside)

E. 辱 5. Jī (Hungry)

F. 秦 6. Lì (Sharp)

#123.

A. 鹫 1. È (Evil)

B. 恶 2. Bì (Certainly)

C. 忆 3. Mèi (Goblin)

D. 魅 4. Jiù (Vulture)

E. 必 5. Guì (Expensive)

F. 贵 6. Yì (Recall)

#124.

A. 斡 1. Hǔ (Tiger)

B. 家 2. Yún (A surname)

C. 郧 3. Jiā (Family)

D. 华 4. Wǎng (Network)

E. 网 5. Huà (Flower)

F. 虎 6. Wò (Turn round)

#125.

A. 孪 1. Fāng (Lane)

B. 郭 2. Yǎn (Nightmare)

C. 魇 3. Luán (Twin)

D. 度 4. Dù (Degree (temperature))

E. 坊 5. Chén (Morning)

F. 晨 6. Guō (A surname)

#126.

A. 帘 1. Yǐ (Lean on or against)

B. 倚 2. Lián (Flag on pole over wine house)

C. 予 3. Zhá (Brake)

D. 露 4. Yú (I)

E. 闸 5. Gé (Skeletons)

F. 骼 6. Lòu (Reveal)

#127.

A. 老 1. Jì (Cross a river)

B. 济 2. Shé (Snake)

C. 更 3. Xiù (Odor)

D. 蛇 4. Lǎo (Aged)

E. 臭　　5. Nüè (Malaria)

F. 疟　　6. Gēng (Change)

#128.

A. 甃　　1. Pán (Tray)

B. 盘　　2. Chà (Differ from)

C. 餍　　3. Yàn (Have had enough (food))

D. 差　　4. Zhòu (Wall of a well)

E. 晷　　5. Guǐ (Sundial)

F. 倒　　6. Dào (Reverse)

#129.

A. 螨　　1. Mǎn (Mite)

B. 丁　　2. Qí (Flag)

C. 匜　　3. Zhēng (Male adult)

D. 旂　　4. Sāng (Funeral)

E. 丧　　5. Yí (Gourd-shaped ladle)

F. 放　　6. Fàng (Release)

#130.

A. 览　　1. Diàn (Door latch)

B. 劣 2. Zuò (Sit)

C. 居 3. Lǎn (Take a look at)

D. 塞 4. Liè (Bad)

E. 系 5. Xì (System)

F. 坐 6. Sāi (Fill in)

#131.

A. 竜 1. Xù (Warm)

B. 屎 2. Shǐ (Excrement)

C. 指 3. Zhǐ (Finger)

D. 饺 4. Zhēng (Seized with terror)

E. 煦 5. Jiǎo (Dumpling)

F. 怔 6. Lóng (Dragon)

#132.

A. 杰 1. Yú (The joint formed by the lateral end of the clavicle of the human body and the acromion of the scapula)

B. 勾 2. Gòu (A surname)

C. 匮 3. Huà (Delimit)

D. 豨 4. Xī (Pig)

E. 髃 5. Jié (Outstanding person)

F. 划 6. Kuì (Deficient)

#133.

A. 馑 1. Shì (Decorate)

B. 辜 2. Pào (Bubble)

C. 则 3. Liào (Name of an ancient state)

D. 廖 4. Zé (Standard)

E. 泡 5. Jǐn (Famine)

F. 饰 6. Gū (Crime)

#134.

A. 搂 1. Lǒu (Hug)

B. 骁 2. Mò (China ink)

C. 丰 3. Jīn (Tianjin)

D. 墨 4. Dá (Tatars)

E. 鞑 5. Xiāo (Valiant)

F. 津 6. Fēng (Abundance)

#135.

A. 飔 1. Mán (Steamed bread)

B. 绠 2. Gěng (A well rope)

C. 馒　　3. Sī (Cool breeze)

D. 绊　　4. Bàn (Cause to trip)

E. 齿　　5. Chǐ (Tooth)

F. 馃　　6. Guǒ (Cake)

#136.

A. 斧　　1. Jiān (Pointed)

B. 琭　　2. Chuàn (String together)

C. 忆　　3. Fǔ (Axe)

D. 肄　　4. Lù (Jade-like stone)

E. 串　　5. Yì (Study)

F. 尖　　6. Yì (Recall)

#137.

A. 拌　　1. Liàng (Cool)

B. 凉　　2. Bàn (Mix)

C. 虚　　3. Mì (Secret)

D. 逻　　4. Luó (Patrol)

E. 秘　　5. Xū (Void)

F. 魆　　6. Xū (Dark)

#138.

A. 乩　　　　1. Diàn (Shop)

B. 汪　　　　2. Jiǎo (Self-respect)

C. 驱　　　　3. Qū (Drive (a horse, car, etc.))

D. 店　　　　4. Guī (Fine jasper)

E. 瑰　　　　5. Wāng (A surname)

F. 糖　　　　6. Táng (Sugar)

#139.

A. 弯　　　　1. Qiáo (Raise)

B. 扑　　　　2. Pū (Attack)

C. 定　　　　3. Yìn (Give water to drink)

D. 饮　　　　4. Wān (Curved)

E. 弄　　　　5. Dìng (Calm)

F. 翘　　　　6. Lòng (Lane)

#140.

A. 骺　　　　1. Qín (A surname)

B. 皈　　　　2. Pēng (Noise of waters)

C. 覃　　　　3. Hóu (Epiphysis)

D. 幻　　　　4. Guī (Be converted to Buddhism)

E. 刘　　5. Liú (A surname)

F. 宷　　6. Huàn (Unreal)

#141.

A. 耩　　1. Bó (Neck)

B. 扈　　2. Zhūn (Grave)

C. 窀　　3. Hù (Retainers)

D. 代　　4. Dài (Take the place of)

E. 膀　　5. Jiǎng (Sow with a drill)

F. 脖　　6. Bǎng (Arm)

#142.

A. 匆　　1. Lú (A surname)

B. 腚　　2. Cōng (Hasty)

C. 洑　　3. Dìng (Buttocks)

D. 老　　4. Lǎo (Aged)

E. 琵　　5. Fù (Swim)

F. 卢　　6. Pí (Lute)

#143.

A. 生　　1. Xū (Petty official)

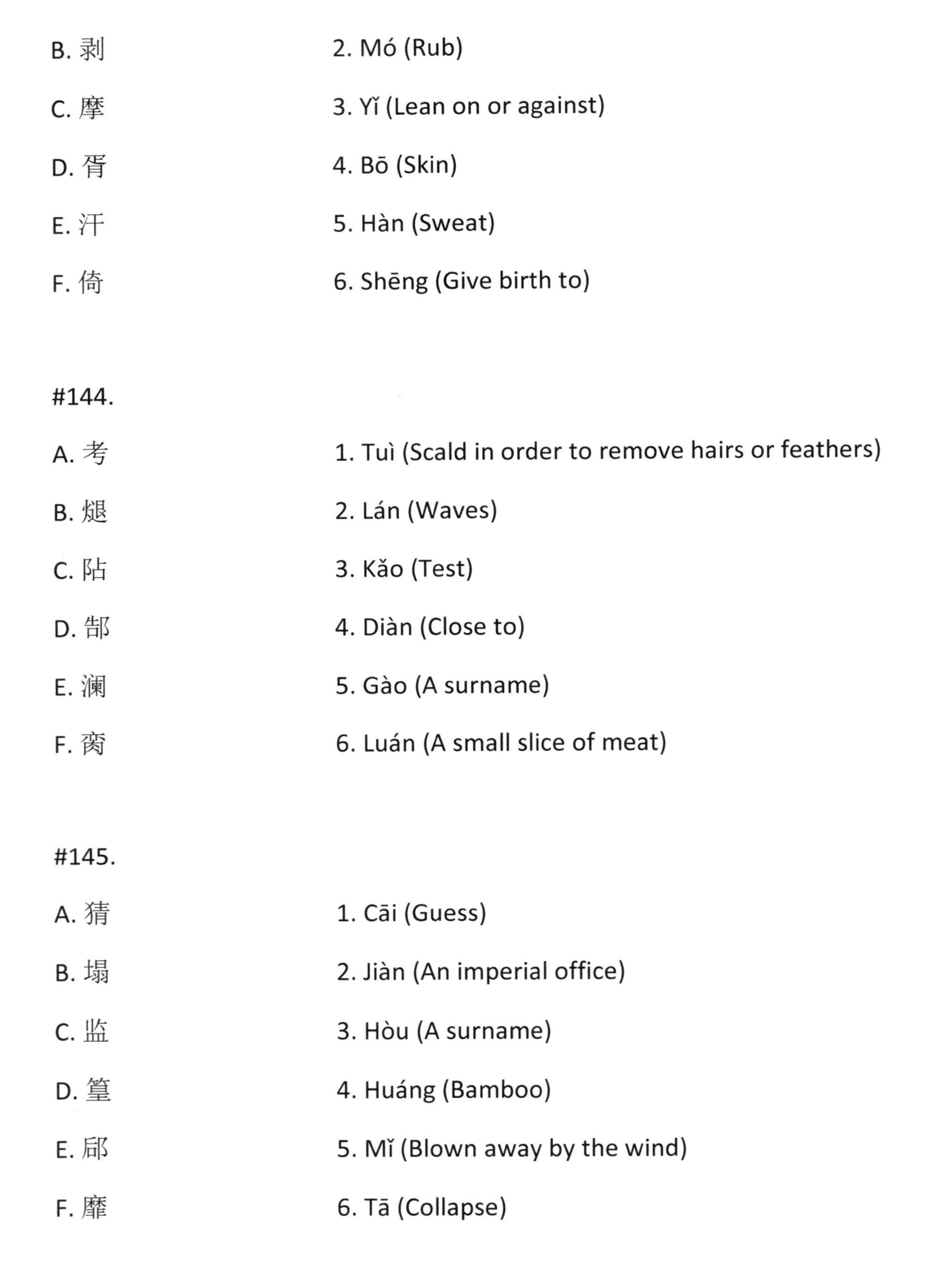

B. 剥 2. Mó (Rub)

C. 摩 3. Yǐ (Lean on or against)

D. 胥 4. Bō (Skin)

E. 汗 5. Hàn (Sweat)

F. 倚 6. Shēng (Give birth to)

#144.

A. 考 1. Tuì (Scald in order to remove hairs or feathers)

B. 煺 2. Lán (Waves)

C. 阽 3. Kǎo (Test)

D. 郜 4. Diàn (Close to)

E. 澜 5. Gào (A surname)

F. 脔 6. Luán (A small slice of meat)

#145.

A. 猜 1. Cāi (Guess)

B. 塌 2. Jiàn (An imperial office)

C. 监 3. Hòu (A surname)

D. 篁 4. Huáng (Bamboo)

E. 郈 5. Mǐ (Blown away by the wind)

F. 靡 6. Tā (Collapse)

#146.

A. 沱　　1. Xuě (Snow)

B. 蜚　　2. Tuó (A small bay in a river)

C. 雪　　3. Fēi (Fly)

D. 翌　　4. Yì (Next)

E. 分　　5. Fēn (Divide)

F. 扃　　6. Jiōng (A bolt or hook for fastening a door from outside)

#147.

A. 窬　　1. Yù (Control)

B. 驭　　2. Jiū (Gather)

C. 勼　　3. Yǎ (Refined)

D. 瘫　　4. Quán (Spring)

E. 泉　　5. Yú (Climb over a wall)

F. 雅　　6. Tān (Palsy)

#148.

A. 平　　1. Píng (Level)

B. 秫　　2. Yuán (A surname)

C. 愐　　3. Shuǎ (Play)

D. 髁 4. Shú (Kaoliang)

E. 沅 5. Kē (Condyle)

F. 要 6. Miǎn (Diligence)

#149.

A. 地 1. Bǎ (Target)

B. 魁 2. Qiāng (Cavity)

C. 卒 3. Dì (The earth)

D. 腔 4. Kuí (Chief)

E. 靶 5. Zāo (Dregs)

F. 糟 6. Zú (Pawn)

#150.

A. 醇 1. Liào (Material)

B. 竟 2. Chún (Mellow wine)

C. 料 3. Zhuǎng (Big and thick)

D. 狡 4. Jìng (Finish)

E. 奘 5. Jiǎo (Crafty)

F. 嚭 6. Pǐ (Mound)

ANSWERS (1-150)

#1.	F. Sà	D. Chuí	B. Jī	#76.	F. Wài	D. Dié	B. Gòu
A. Jiǔ		E. Yún	C. Huáng	A. Yì		E. Yìn	C. Kuì
B. Mèi	#20.	F. Jiān	D. Niàn	B. Shān	#95.	F. Chéng	D. Xī
C. Shī	A. Lěi		E. Zuò	C. Tán	A. Bī		E. Yú
D. Xù	B. Hóng	#39.	F. Yīng	D. Bò	B. Rén	#114.	F. Huà
E. Yù	C. Liáo	A. Qiè		E. Bǎng	C. Qián	A. Mò	
F. Bó	D. Mǎng	B. Shū	#58.	F. Dí	D. Yuán	B. Chà	#133.
	E. Duì	C. Xìng	A. Jī		E. Líng	C. Fèi	A. Jǐn
#2.	F. Zài	D. Huái	B. Jiāng	#77.	F. Bǎ	D. È	B. Gū
A. Jǐng		E. Jǐn	C. Fèn	A. Zǐ		E. Gài	C. Zé
B. Hán	#21.	F. Má	D. Zhā	B. Lóng	#96.	F. Wū	D. Liào
C. Xiōng	A. Còu		E. Dié	C. Hú	A. Shuò		E. Pào
D. Cháng	B. Yì	#40.	F. Píng	D. Ǎo	B. Yù	#115.	F. Shì
E. Tóu	C. Qī	A. Xiāo		E. Qū	C. Yōu	A. Jí	
F. Guà	D. Sù	B. Xiè	#59.	F. Shǐ	D. Jì	B. Wéi	#134.
	E. Jià	C. Tái	A. Fú		E. Wǎn	C. Shè	A. Lǒu
#3.	F. Tǎn	D. Tiǎo	B. Jiāo	#78.	F. Kěn	D. Fěi	B. Xiāo
A. Xiǎn		E. Nòng	C. Tiǎo	A. Xī		E. Xiàng	C. Fēng
B. Lù	#22.	F. Jiǔ	D. Zhěn	B. Hé	#97.	F. Yǎn	D. Mò
C. Bā	A. Wěn		E. Bì	C. Gāng	A. Shì		E. Dá
D. Qìn	B. Gàn	#41.	F. Liáo	D. Shuǎng	B. Gé	#116.	F. Jīn
E. Bèi	C. Dān	A. Yíng		E. Pǐ	C. Èi	A. Guāi	
F. Wēi	D. Yǐn	B. Tǐng	#60.	F. Jì	D. Yē	B. Qiǎng	#135.
	E. Tǔn	C. Yǔn	A. Xún		E. Táng	C. Tī	A. Sī
#4.	F. Pù	D. Bǐ	B. Jǐng	#79.	F. Jiè	D. Sù	B. Gěng
A. Shēng		E. Gè	C. Bā	A. Pō		E. Nài	C. Mán
B. Rèn	#23.	F. Tā	D. Shěn	B. Pào	#98.	F. Jìng	D. Bàn
C. Yě	A. Zhū		E. Zhuàn	C. Lì	A. Miǎn		E. Chǐ
D. Zhào	B. Huī	#42.	F. Kàng	D. Niáng	B. Huó	#117.	F. Guǒ
E. Jì	C. Jùn	A. Lěi		E. Lú	C. Liú	A. Zhuō	
F. Zhān	D. Guī	B. Capture	#61.	F. Diǎn	D. Mò	B. Dié	#136.
	E. Jì	C. Shā	A. Bó		E. Zhǐ	C. Bìng	A. Fǔ

#5.	F. Yì	D. É	B. Jīng	#80.	F. Liǎo	D. Jì	B. Lù
A. Lǎng		E. Fú	C. Yáng	A. Pēng		E. Kuí	C. Yì
B. Wèi	#24.	F. Sǔn	D. Lǐ	B. Gēng	#99.	F. Huī	D. Yì
C. Yǎ	A. Wū		E. Fù	C. Gū	A. Xí		E. Chuàn
D. Hé	B. Ké	#43.	F. Bāo	D. Tián	B. Sàn	#118.	F. Jiān
E. Huí	C. Shú	A. Nàn		E. Shēn	C. Yóu	A. Nài	
F. Tián	D. Zhī	B. Xiōng	#62.	F. Miè	D. Bǎi	B. Xīng	#137.
	E. Piān	C. Píng	A. Lóng		E. Jī	C. Nā	A. Bàn
#6.	F. Biàn	D. Tào	B. Qiú	#81.	F. Xíng	D. Jiǔ	B. Liàng
A. Hún		E. Wò	C. Chuǎi	A. Zhí		E. Máng	C. Xū
B. Yì	#25.	F. Xiè	D. Bīn	B. Jiù	#100.	F. Gǔ	D. Luó
C. Suǒ	A. Gěng		E. Gǎn	C. Nuó	A. Měi		E. Mì
D. Tīng	B. Ěr	#44.	F. Jiǎo	D. Dú	B. Líng	#119.	F. Xū
E. Lòu	C. Mèi	A. Hán		E. Gū	C. Lǒu	A. Gòu	
F. Miǎn	D. Jǐ	B. Yǐ	#63.	F. Jīn	D. Yáo	B. Mèi	#138.
	E. Guǎn	C. Lòu	A. Zǐ		E. Lèi	C. Èi	A. Jiǎo
#7.	F. Wèi	D. Zé	B. Méi	#82.	F. Yāo	D. Kòu	B. Wāng
A. Méi		E. Xuán	C. Gū	A. Cāng		E. Dīng	C. Qū
B. Máng	#26.	F. Zī	D. Mǎi	B. Kào	#101.	F. Yǐn	D. Diàn
C. Niào	A. Zhuó		E. Bì	C. Ruǎn	A. Hán		E. Guī
D. Tiǎo	B. Liú	#45.	F. Què	D. Xī	B. Guó	#120.	F. Táng
E. Zhì	C. Dàn	A. Tì		E. Qù	C. Méng	A. Shē	
F. Táng	D. Lì	B. Hé	#64.	F. Qīn	D. Yù	B. Bì	#139.
	E. Yàn	C. Jiù	A. Shān		E. Duǒ	C. Zài	A. Wān
#8.	F. Huàn	D. Jī	B. Còu	#83.	F. Jī	D. Dǎo	B. Pū
A. Hé		E. Biǎo	C. Mǐn	A. Chāng		E. Sì	C. Dìng
B. Nán	#27.	F. Yā	D. Bó	B. Mǎng	#102.	F. Lí	D. Yìn
C. Zhǐ	A. Shǎng		E. Pǐ	C. Xì	A. Jiā		E. Lòng
D. Fù	B. Jǔ	#46.	F. Zào	D. Kuàng	B. Jí	#121.	F. Qiáo
E. Bǐng	C. Xiàn	A. Shā		E. Zhuàng	C. Jì	A. Nài	
F. Péi	D. Fǎng	B. Chá	#65.	F. Chéng	D. Zhī	B. Mán	#140.

	E. Léi	C. Hái	A. Zī		E. Rǔ	C. Fǎn	A. Hóu
#9.	F. Gòng	D. Hào	B. Bèn	#84.	F. Dù	D. Hū	B. Guī
A. Sūn		E. Yìn	C. Biǎo	A. Yú		E. Tí	C. Qín
B. Yǎ	#28.	F. Jiē	D. Zhí	B. Fén	#103.	F. Xiàn	D. Huàn
C. Sū	A. Shǔ		E. Wō	C. Shèn	A. Kāi		E. Liú
D. Chuán	B. Yāo	#47.	F. Huī	D. Guàn	B. Jiū	#122.	F. Pēng
E. Ér	C. Lǐ	A. Jiè		E. Yì	C. Jiàn	A. Jī	
F. Qiān	D. Bèi	B. Zōng	#66.	F. Bó	D. Wèi	B. Jiù	#141.
	E. Nián	C. Bò	A. Wàng		E. Xī	C. Lì	A. Jiǎng
#10.	F. Shuāng	D. Tí	B. Nì	#85.	F. Jiù	D. Wài	B. Hù
A. Chà		E. Cháng	C. Biào	A. Gē		E. Rǔ	C. Zhūn
B. Tí	#29.	F. Mí	D. De	B. Shí	#104.	F. Qín	D. Dài
C. Yuè	A. Mò		E. Zhǐ	C. Bèn	A. Méi		E. Bǎng
D. Rǎn	B. Yì	#48.	F. Qiǎng	D. Tuǐ	B. Dài	#123.	F. Bó
E. Lā	C. Xiè	A. Qiāo		E. Shū	C. Luò	A. Jiù	
F. Din	D. Xūn	B. Pēng	#67.	F. Tán	D. Zhǎng	B. È	#142.
	E. Lóu	C. Ēi	A. Jī		E. Shòu	C. Yì	A. Cōng
#11.	F. Sà	D. Qué	B. Xiè	#86.	F. gé	D. Mèi	B. Dìng
A. Yì		E. Xìng	C. Yān	A. Tiǎn		E. Bì	C. Fù
B. Dǎn	#30.	F. Xiàn	D. Zhuō	B. Zhì	#105.	F. Guì	D. Lǎo
C. Zhuàng	A. Mǐ		E. Shǐ	C. Fěi	A. Lǚ		E. Pí
D. Niǎn	B. Chú	#49.	F. Zuò	D. Huàn	B. Pèi	#124.	F. Lú
E. Sū	C. Qǐ	A. Mó		E. Mò	C. Shì	A. Wò	
F. Zōu	D. Liáo	B. Yǔn	#68.	F. Bāo	D. Yān	B. Jiā	#143.
	E. Zhài	C. Yāng	A. Fàn		E. Qiě	C. Yún	A. Shēng
#12.	F. Zǐ	D. Tàng	B. Gōng	#87.	F. Nàn	D. Huà	B. Bō
A. Shàn		E. Gài	C. Fāng	A. Shā		E. Wǎng	C. Mó
B. Lóng	#31.	F. Zhì	D. Wù	B. Biàn	#106.	F. Hǔ	D. Xū
C. Lì	A. Bāo		E. Yù	C. Zhèn	A. Mò		E. Hàn
D. Wū	B. Jī	#50.	F. Guà	D. Xíng	B. Zhòng	#125.	F. Yǐ
E. Bà	C. Wèi	A. Pèi		E. Fǎ	C. Hán	A. Luán	
F. Qǐ	D. Xùn	B. Tàng	#69.	F. Chào	D. Jìn	B. Guō	#144.
	E. Kū	C. Shà	A. Éi		E. Nìng	C. Yǎn	A. Kǎo
#13.	F. Jiē	D. Zhà	B. Yù	#88.	F. Yōu	D. Dù	B. Tuì

A. Bù		E. Táo	C. Mò	A. Bèng		E. Fāng	C. Diàn
B. Pá	#32.	F. Rǔ	D. Liǎn	B. Sī	#107.	F. Chén	D. Gào
C. Páng	A. Xiè		E. Shùn	C. Guì	A. Bà		E. Lán
D. Zé	B. Zuǎn	#51.	F. Dǎo	D. Lǎn	B. Jiǎo	#126.	F. Luán
E. Lēi	C. Yù	A. Zài		E. Huàn	C. Fēng	A. Lián	
F. Liǎn	D. Gē	B. Kāi	#70.	F. Nǎi	D. Fú	B. Yǐ	#145.
	E. Lì	C. Yuán	A. Má		E. Lí	C. Yú	A. Cāi
#14.	F. Téng	D. Běn	B. Wò	#89.	F. Yán	D. Lòu	B. Tā
A. Guì		E. Shān	C. Mài	A. Háo		E. Zhá	C. Jiàn
B. Huī	#33.	F. Fǎng	D. Bèi	B. Zuò	#108.	F. Gé	D. Huáng
C. Liè	A. Qiào		E. Yùn	C. Gū	A. Fēn		E. Hòu
D. Ér	B. Rǔ	#52.	F. Xī	D. Mèng	B. Hú	#127.	F. Mǐ
E. Táo	C. Yì	A. Jiū		E. Bà	C. Mǔ	A. Lǎo	
F. Táng	D. Qié	B. Yáng	#71.	F. Xún	D. Què	B. Jì	#146.
	E. Zhà	C. Yuān	A. Zuò		E. gé	C. Gēng	A. Tuó
#15.	F. Lù	D. Nüè	B. Yóu	#90.	F. Ruǎn	D. Shé	B. Fēi
A. Fù		E. Wū	C. Lì	A. Ěr		E. Xiù	C. Xuě
B. Jī	#34.	F. Suǒ	D. Shàn	B. Tái	#109.	F. Nüè	D. Yì
C. Bǎn	A. Dài		E. Zuò	C. Láng	A. Xiā		E. Fēn
D. Mā	B. Zhǐ	#53.	F. Jiào	D. Zàng	B. Zhòu	#128.	F. Jiōng
E. Kūn	C. Pù	A. Chén		E. Tiān	C. Jì	A. Zhòu	
F. Pà	D. Yì	B. Bèi	#72.	F. Xiàn	D. Wāng	B. Pán	#147.
	E. Guǐ	C. Yì	A. Fú		E. Kǎo	C. Yàn	A. Yú
#16.	F. Liǎo	D. Chǎn	B. Shè	#91.	F. Sù	D. Chà	B. Yù
A. Āi		E. Zhǒng	C. Yǐn	A. Shèng		E. Guǐ	C. Jiū
B. Hū	#35.	F. Běn	D. Guāi	B. Càn	#110.	F. Dào	D. Tān
C. Tóng	A. Zàng		E. Kè	C. Xiǎn	A. Fáng		E. Quán
D. Qì	B. Nǎi	#54.	F. Gēng	D. Luō	B. Běi	#129.	F. Yǎ
E. Chí	C. Jiǒng	A. Zhǎng		E. Xiàn	C. Shāo	A. Mǎn	
F. Gào	D. Xiān	B. Lún	#73.	F. Chuō	D. Jì	B. Zhēng	#148.
	E. Chī	C. Méi	A. Yù		E. Huán	C. Yí	A. Píng
#17.	F. Fú	D. Gāng	B. Sì	#92.	F. Tuǒ	D. Qí	B. Shú
A. Tóu		E. Shè	C. Yìn	A. Chá		E. Sāng	C. Miǎn
B. Jī	#36.	F. Jú	D. Zhū	B. Què	#111.	F. Fàng	D. Kē

C. Yàn	A. Jiě		E. Qì	C. Yǐng	A. Xì		E. Yuán
D. Yé	B. Jǐng	#55.	F. Shān	D. Lìng	B. Mò	#130.	F. Shuǎ
E. Piān	C. Hōng	A. Hú		E. Pào	C. Hù	A. Lǎn	
F. Lěi	D. Chǐ	B. Jūn	#74.	F. Xù	D. Yā	B. Liè	#149.
	E. Zhì	C. Sī	A. Zǎo		E. Shéng	C. Diàn	A. Dì
#18.	F. Cì	D. Shuāng	B. Xuàn	#93.	F. Tì	D. Sāi	B. Kuí
A. Lín		E. Dá	C. Hún	A. Xī		E. Xì	C. Zú
B. Hén	#37.	F. Jù	D. Suì	B. Nài	#112.	F. Zuò	D. Qiāng
C. Zàng	A. Cuī		E. Cōng	C. Lóng	A. Shǐ		E. Bǎ
D. Xiáng	B. Gāng	#56.	F. Wù	D. Bèi	B. Wài	#131.	F. Zāo
E. Wēn	C. Dá	A. Pí		E. Shěn	C. Cháng	A. Lóng	
F. Mí	D. Dì	B. Fán	#75.	F. Wèi	D. Yǐ	B. Shǐ	#150.
	E. Yáng	C. Bèi	A. Hé		E. Gān	C. Zhǐ	A. Chún
#19.	F. Zú	D. Gǔ	B. Zǎo	#94.	F. Guǎn	D. Jiǎo	B. Jìng
A. Sù		E. Chāo	C. Huà	A. Dài		E. Xù	C. Liào
B. Dāng	#38.	F. Bèi	D. Chóng	B. Yóu	#113.	F. Zhēng	D. Jiǎo
C. Jiǎo	A. Xié		E. Lì	C. Zāng	A. Yè		E. Zhuǎng
D. Fū	B. Kuàng	#57.	F. Zhòng	D. Qū	B. Jià	#132.	F. Pǐ
E. Jiě	C. Zhān	A. Chéng		E. Huī	C. Liù	A. Jié	

Milton Keynes UK
Ingram Content Group UK Ltd.
UKHW050641221123
432980UK00014B/780